DOGS DON'T EAT DESSERT

PEANUTS®
featuring
"Good ol' CharlieBrown"
by SCHULZ
SKI
LIFT
© 1984 United Feature Syndicate, Inc.

This edition first published by Ravette Books Limited 1987
Reprinted 1988

Printed and bound for Ravette Books Limited,
3 Glenside Estate, Star Road,
Partridge Green, Horsham,
Sussex RH13 8RA
by The Guernsey Press Company Limited,
Guernsey, Channel Islands.

ISBN 1 85304 009 6

DOGS DON'T EAT DESSERT

BUT WE LIKE TO BE ASKED

Charles M. Schulz

RAVETTE BOOKS

PEANUTS
featuring
"Good ol' CharlieBrown"
by SCHULZ
STUPID TREE!
NOT AGAIN!?!
EVERY SHOT I HIT SEEMS TO END UP BEHIND A TREE..
© 1985 United Feature Syndicate, Inc.

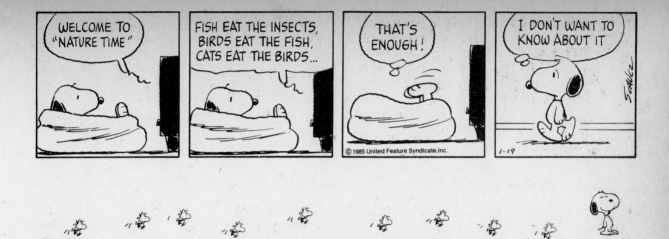

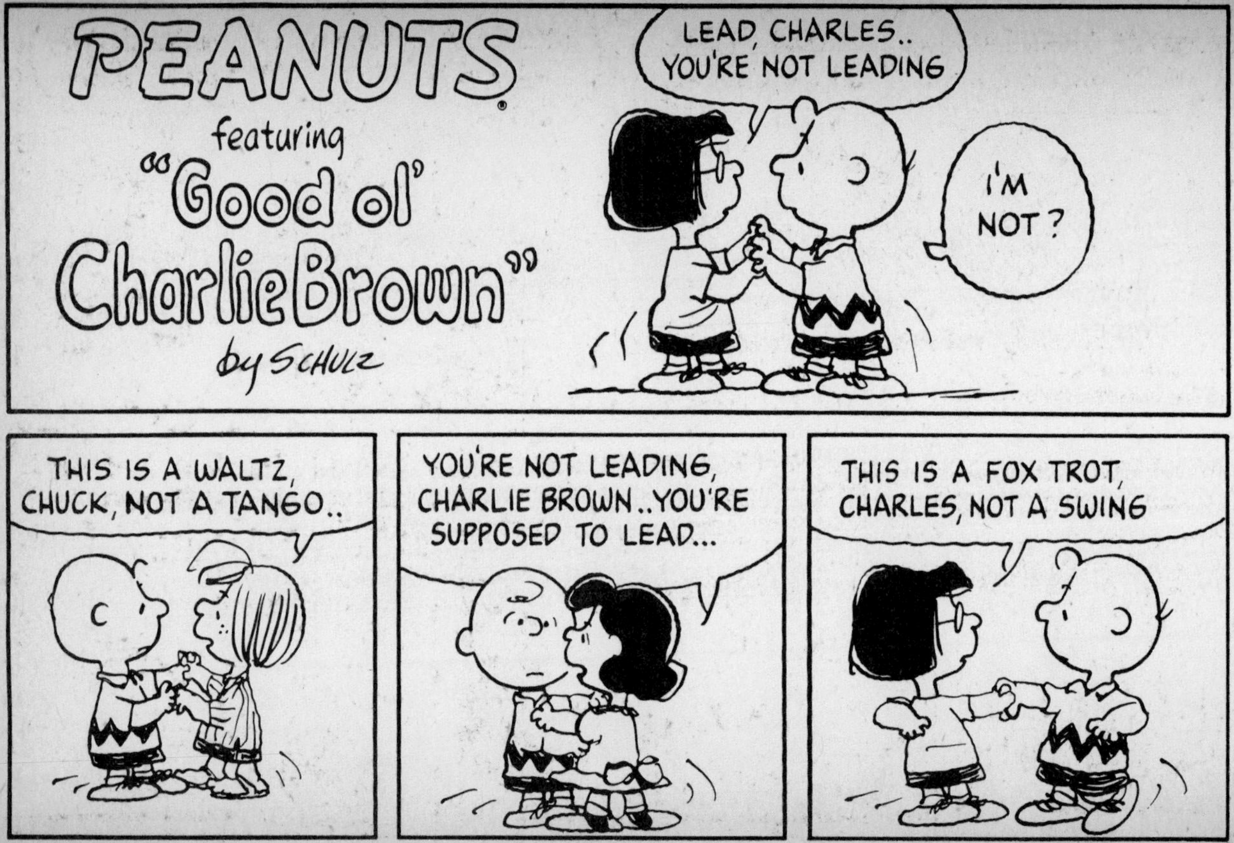
PEANUTS
featuring "Good ol' Charlie Brown"
by SCHULZ
LEAD, CHARLES.. YOU'RE NOT LEADING
I'M NOT?
THIS IS A WALTZ, CHUCK, NOT A TANGO..
YOU'RE NOT LEADING, CHARLIE BROWN..YOU'RE SUPPOSED TO LEAD...
THIS IS A FOX TROT, CHARLES, NOT A SWING

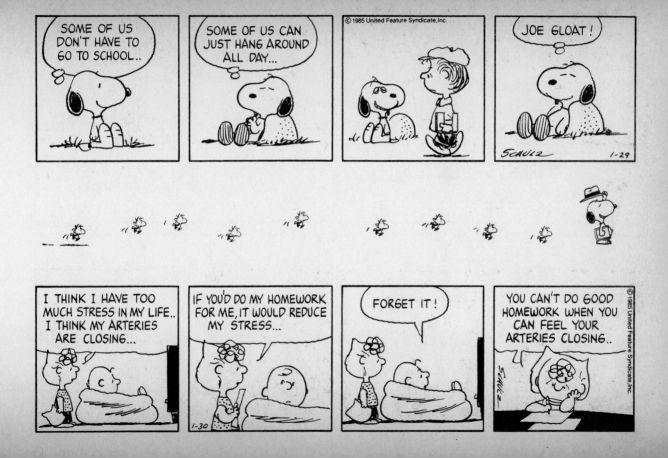

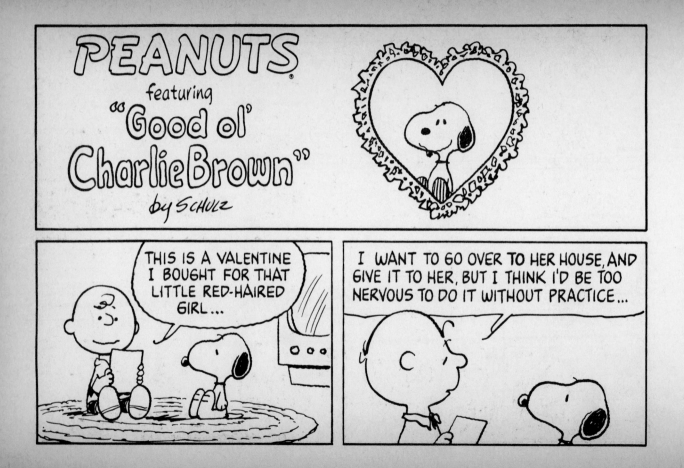

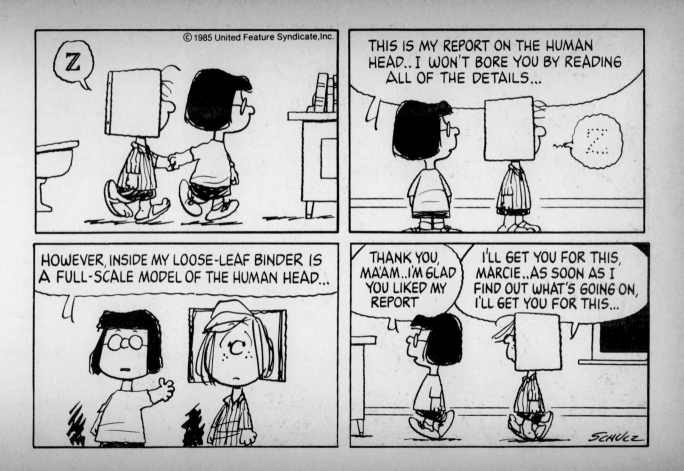

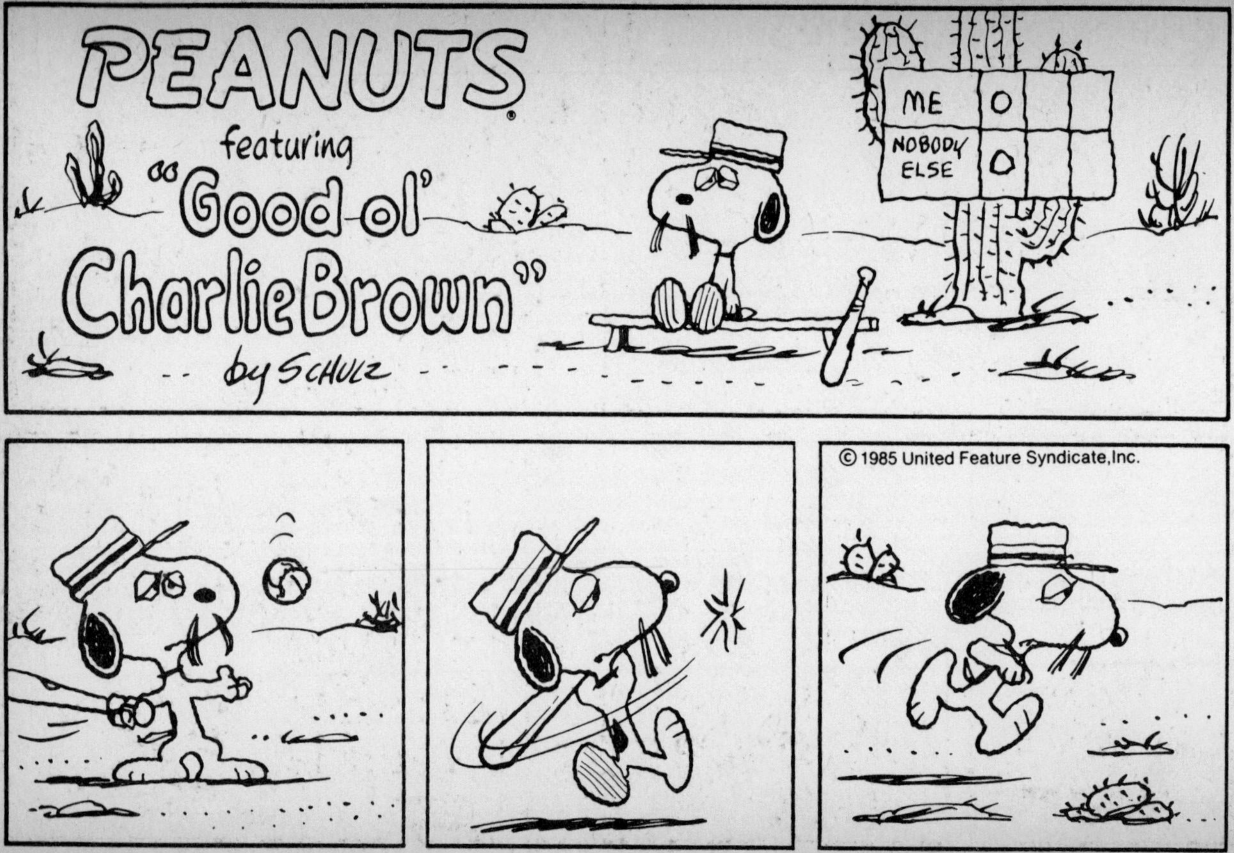
PEANUTS®
featuring
"Good ol' Charlie Brown"
by SCHULZ
ME
O
NOBODY ELSE
O
© 1985 United Feature Syndicate, Inc.

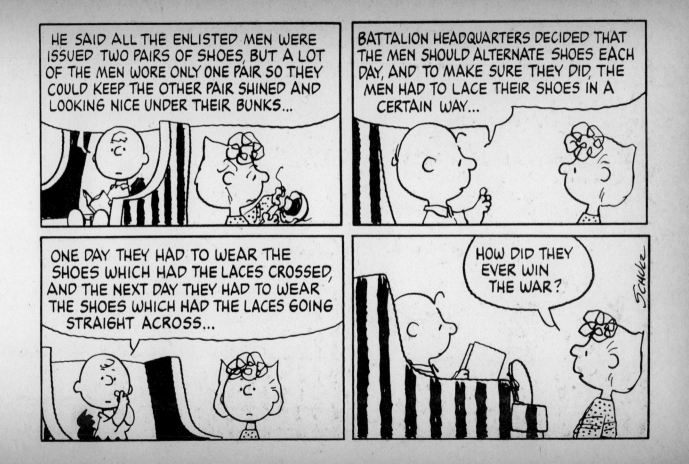

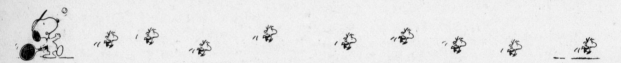

PEANUTS
featuring
"Good ol' Charlie Brown"
by SCHULZ
A POP FLY!
I GOT IT! IT'S ALL MINE!
3-10
IF I CATCH THIS BALL, WE'LL WIN OUR FIRST GAME OF THE SEASON..
PLEASE LET ME CATCH IT! PLEASE LET ME BE THE HERO! PLEASE LET ME CATCH IT! PLEASE!

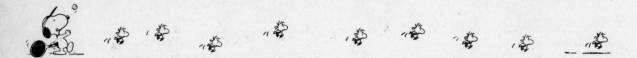

PEANUTS
featuring "Good ol' Charlie Brown"
by SCHULZ
?
NO, OVER HERE..
THIS WAS THE ONE..
THIS IS THE TREE WHERE YOU WERE BORN..I REMEMBER HOW TALL IT WAS..
3-17

PEANUTS®
featuring "Good ol' Charlie Brown"
by SCHULZ
NO, MA'AM
I'M SO ASHAMED OF MYSELF
3-24
© 1985 United Feature Syndicate, Inc.
I TOLD THE TEACHER I DIDN'T HAVE MY HOMEWORK DONE BECAUSE I WASN'T FEELING WELL LAST NIGHT..

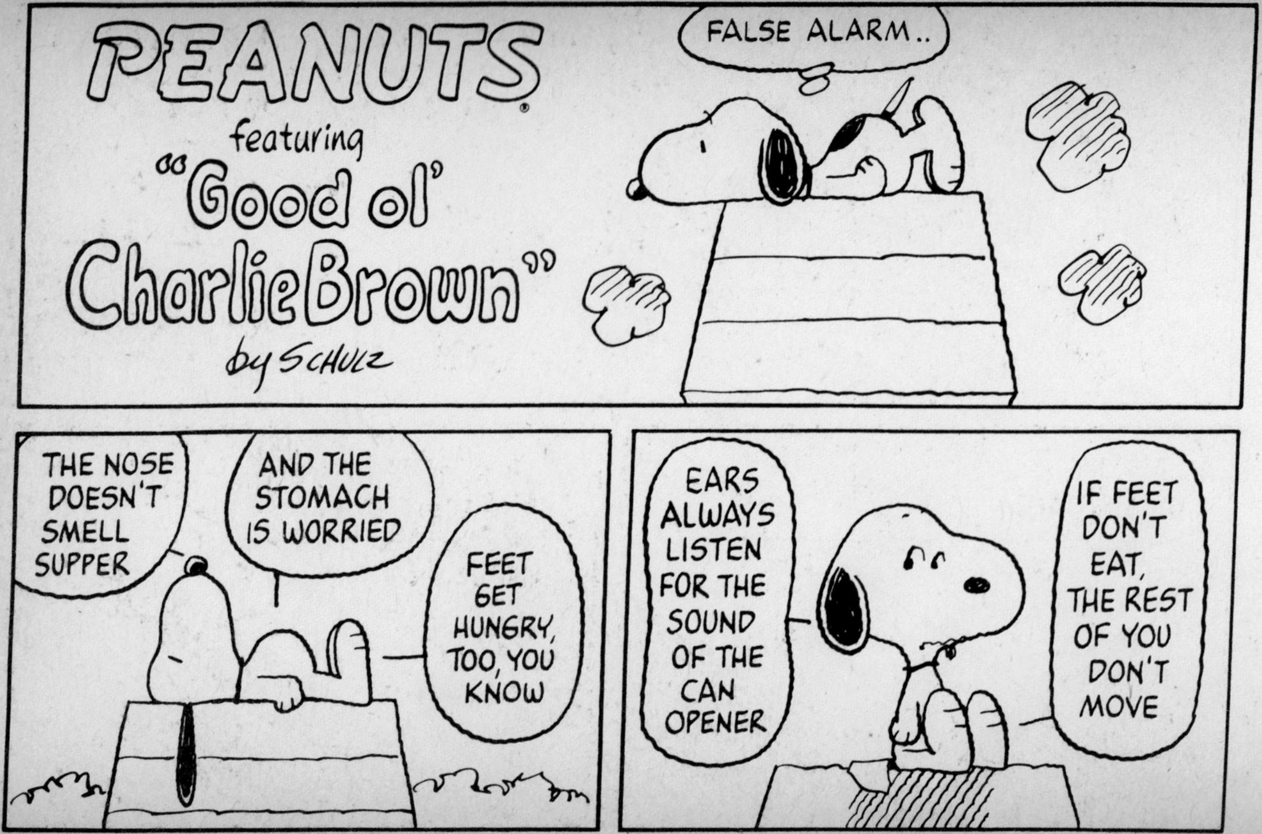
PEANUTS
featuring "Good ol' Charlie Brown"
by SCHULZ
FALSE ALARM..
THE NOSE DOESN'T SMELL SUPPER
AND THE STOMACH IS WORRIED
FEET GET HUNGRY, TOO, YOU KNOW
EARS ALWAYS LISTEN FOR THE SOUND OF THE CAN OPENER
IF FEET DON'T EAT, THE REST OF YOU DON'T MOVE

EYES LIKE TO SEE A GOOD SUPPER
IF SUPPER IS LATE, THOUGH, IT'S THE STOMACH WHO SUFFERS
WHAT ABOUT TOES? IF TOES DON'T EAT, TOES DON'T WIGGLE..
BAD NEWS..WE'RE OUT OF DOG FOOD SO I HAVE TO RUN DOWN TO THE STORE... I'LL BE BACK IN ABOUT TEN MINUTES...
I HOPE YOU UNDERSTAND..
3-31
I UNDERSTAND, BUT HOW AM I GOING TO EXPLAIN IT TO THE TROOPS?
SCHULZ
© 1985 United Feature Syndicate, Inc.

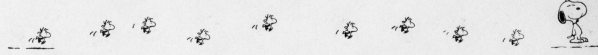

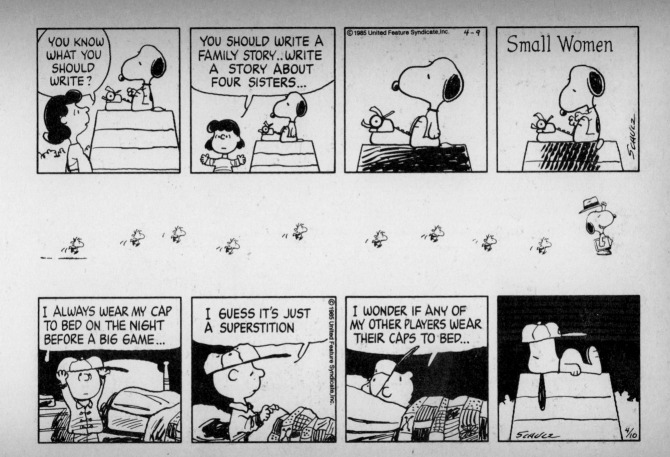

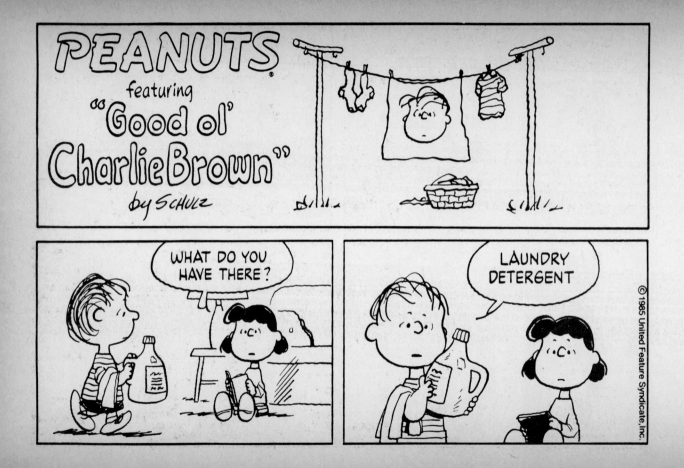

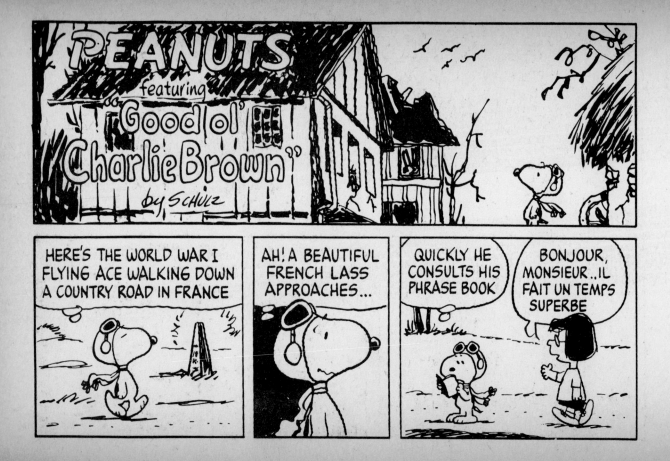

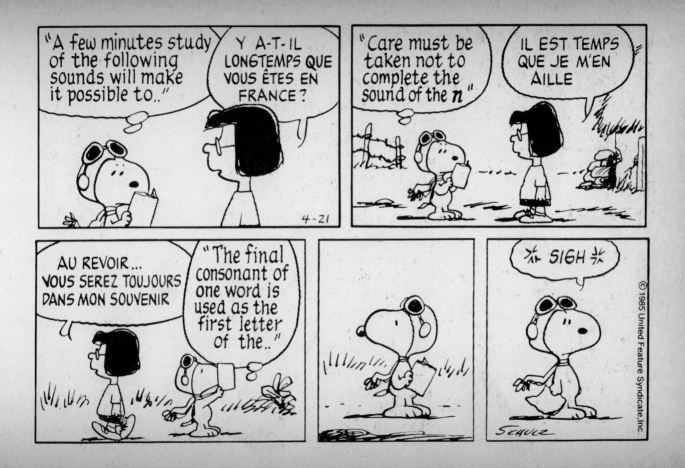

PEANUTS®
featuring "Good ol' Charlie Brown"
by SCHULZ
BEWARE OF SOME DOGS
YOU'RE COMING OVER? GREAT! COME RIGHT IN THROUGH OUR BACK GATE
DOG? YES, I HAVE A DOG, BUT DON'T WORRY ABOUT HIM
© 1985 United Feature Syndicate, Inc.

PEANUTS
featuring
"Good ol' Charlie Brown"
by SCHULZ
THESE ARE COMMAS AND THESE ARE POSSESSIVES..COMMAS DO ALL THE WORK AND POSSESSIVES GET ALL THE CREDIT..THEY HATE EACH OTHER!

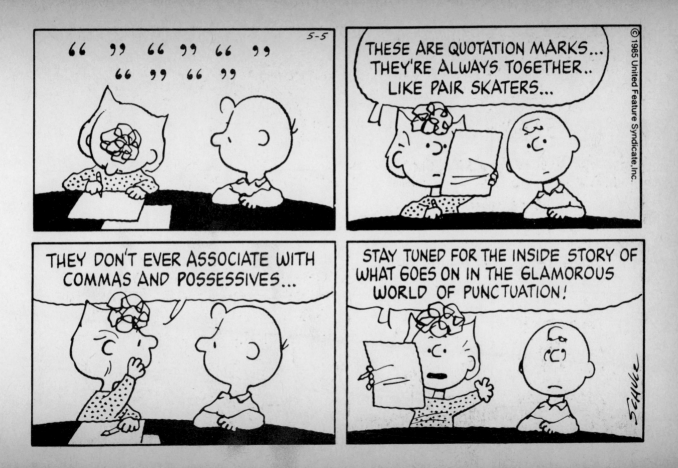

PEANUTS
featuring
"Good ol' Charlie Brown"
by SCHULZ
YOU SIT HERE WITH THE FLOWER, AND IF YOUR MOTHER FLIES OVER, YOU REACH UP AND HAND IT TO HER..MAKE SURE YOU SAY, "HAPPY MOTHER'S DAY"
WE'D BETTER PRACTICE IT ONCE...
I'LL BE YOUR MOTHER, AND I'LL COME FLYING OVER, OKAY ?

5-12
© 1985 United Feature Syndicate, Inc.
HI, SONNY! IT'S ME, YOUR MOM! WHAT A PRETTY FLOWER...
HAND IT TO ME! QUICK!!
BONK
MAYBE SHE'LL JUST COME WALKING BY..
SCHULZ

5-9
© 1985 United Feature Syndicate, Inc.
SCHULZ

I LOVE GOING OVER TO WOODSTOCK'S NEST TO WATCH TV...
5-10
© 1985 United Feature Syndicate, Inc.
HE'S THE ONLY ONE WHO HAS A SATELLITE DISH..
SCHULZ

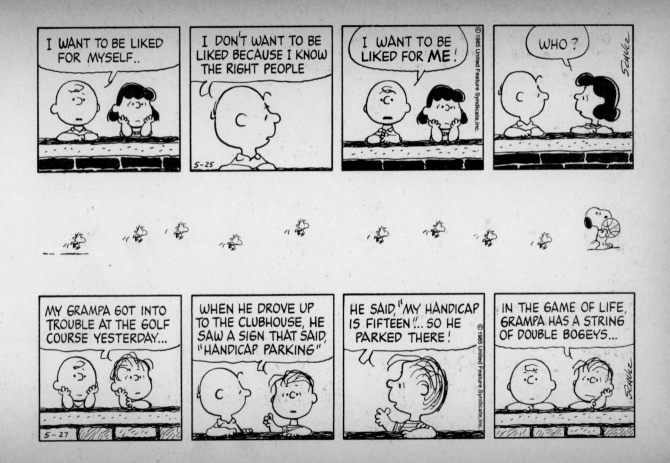

PEANUTS
featuring
"Good ol' Charlie Brown"
by SCHULZ
Dear Dad,
Guess what...
OUCH!
© 1985 United Feature Syndicate, Inc.
I have joined a square dance group.
OW!

We meet once a week...
OUCH!
We hold hands, and dance around and around.
YIPE!!
6-16
Anyway, Happy Father's Day! your son, Spike
OUCH!
P.S. Please excuse my shaking. I am writing with my left hand.
SCHULZ

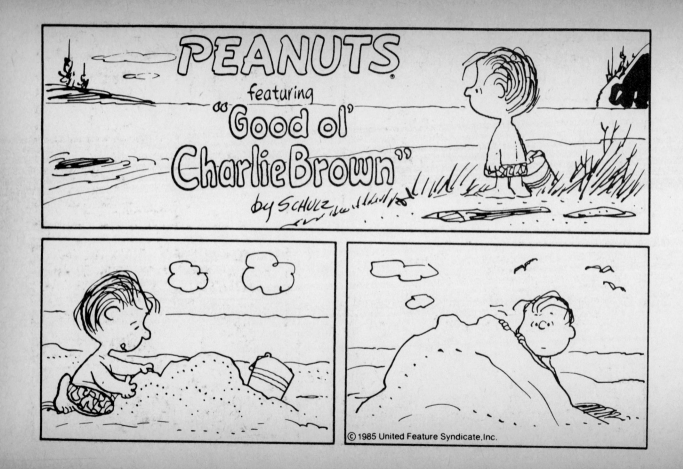

Other Snoopy titles published by Ravette Books

Black and white landscapes
It's a Dog's Life   £2.50
Roundup   £2.50
Freewheelin'   £2.50
Joe Cool   £2.50
You're on the Wrong Foot Again, Charlie Brown   £2.50

Snoopy Stars
No. 1   Snoopy Stars as The Flying Ace   £1.95
No. 2   Snoopy Stars as The Matchmaker   £1.95
No. 3   Snoopy Stars as The Terror of the Ice   £1.95
No. 4   Snoopy Stars as The Legal Beagle   £1.95
No. 5   Snoopy Stars as The Fearless Leader   £1.95
No. 6   Snoopy Stars as Man's Best Friend   £1.95

Colour landscapes
First Serve   £2.95
Be Prepared   £2.95
Stay Cool   £2.95
Shall We Dance?   £2.95
Let's Go   £2.95
Come Fly With Me   £2.95

All these books are available at your local bookshop or news-agent, or can be ordered direct from the publisher. Just tick the titles you require and fill in the form below. Prices and availability subject to change without notice.

Ravette Books Limited, 3 Glenside Estate, Star Road, Partridge Green, Horsham, West Sussex RH13 8RA

Please send a cheque or postal order, and allow the following for postage and packing. UK: 45p for one book plus 30p for each additional book.

Name ....

Address ....

....